KT-230-019

WAKEFIELD LIBRARIES

30000010237945

This Book
Belongs to:

....

....

Consultant: Fiona Moss, RE Adviser at RE Today Services
Editor: Cathy Jones
Designer: Chris Fraser

Copyright © QED Publishing 2012

First published in the UK in 2012 by
QED Publishing
A Quarto Group company
230 City Road
London EC1V 2TT

www.qed-publishing.co.uk

All rights reserved. No part of this publication may be reproduced,
stored in a retrieval system, or transmitted in any form or by any means,
electronic, mecwhanical, photocopying, recording, or
otherwise, without the prior permission of the publisher, nor be
otherwise circulated in any form of binding or cover other than
that in which it is published and without a similar condition
being imposed on the subsequent purchaser.

A catalogue record for this book is available
from the British Library.

ISBN 978 1 84835 851 5

Printed in China

WAKEFIELD LIBRARIES & INFO. SERVICES	
30000010237945	
Bertrams	30/08/2012
J221.95	£8.99

Noah's Ark

Written by Katherine Sully

Illustrated by Simona Sanfilippo

QED Publishing

Old man Noah was a very good man.

He loved God and always listened to what God told him. God loved Noah because he was good.

But God was not happy with the rest of the people.
They didn't listen and behaved very badly.

One day, God said to Noah, "I am going to flood the earth to wash it clean. Build a wooden ark and make sure it will not leak.

"Take your family and two of every kind of animal into the ark.

Bring plenty of food for everyone. In seven days I will make it rain."

So Noah did as God told him.
His sons Shem, Ham
and Japheth helped.

They chopped
down trees.

They hammered
in pegs.

They sawed big planks.

They painted
the ark so that it
would not leak.

They all worked very hard until the ark was finished.

But there was no time to rest.
Next, they collected two of every kind
of animal. It wasn't easy!

Two by two the
animals crept or slithered
or plodded or hopped onto the ark.

They made a terrible noise!

Squawk!

Baa!

Sssssssss!

And when they were all inside,
God shut the door.

Sure enough, after seven days, it began to rain.
Drip, drop – the rain didn't stop!
The water rose and lifted the ark.

For forty days and forty nights it rained. Even the highest mountains were flooded.

Inside the ark it was dark.
All the animals squashed
together and
they made
a terrible
noise!

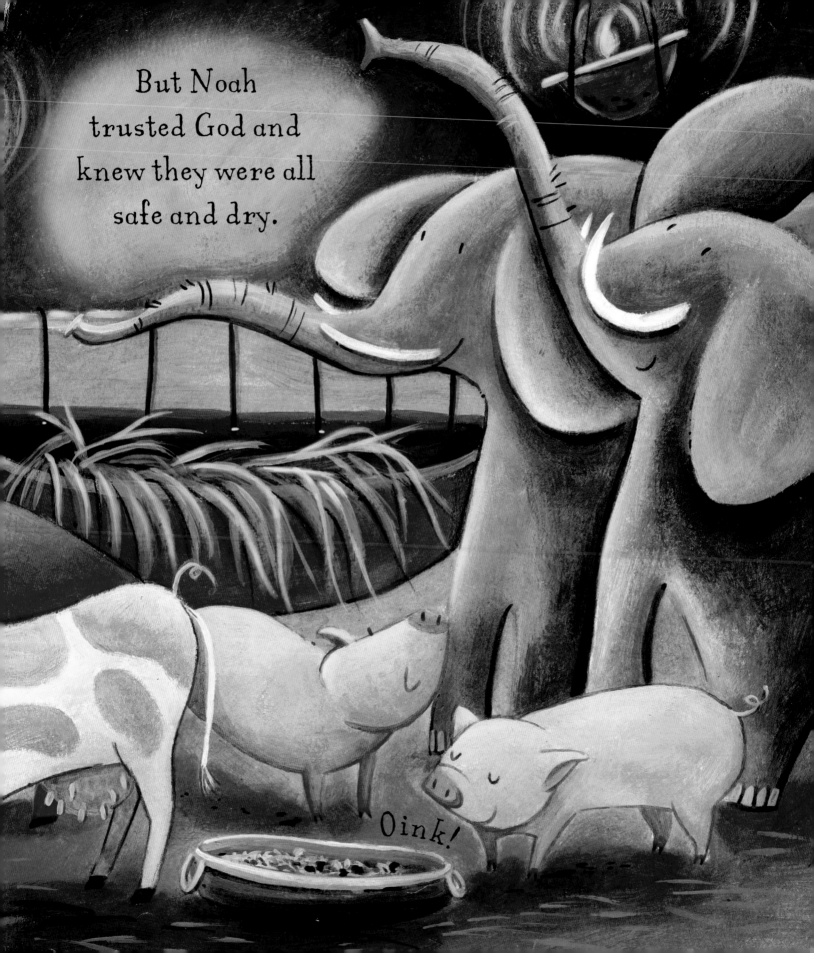

But Noah trusted God and knew they were all safe and dry.

Oink!

For another hundred and fifty days the earth was flooded and washed clean. But God did not forget Noah and his ark.

Drip, drop – the rain DID stop!

Then God sent a wind
and the flood went down.
Finally, the ark landed on the
top of the highest mountain.

Slowly, the water went down and down.
Noah opened the window and saw
other mountain tops.

He sent out
a dove, but
the dove soon
flew back.

A week later,
Noah sent out
the dove again.

This time it flew back
carrying a twig in its beak.

Noah waited another week
and sent out the dove again.

This time it didn't fly back. At last,
the dove had found dry land.

Then God said to Noah,
"It's safe to come out now."

Two by two, the animals
came out of the ark into
the sunshine.

Harrumph!

Growl!

Sssssss!

Squeak!

Noah thanked God
for keeping them all safe.

Squawk!

After that, God made a promise to Noah never to flood the earth again.

As a sign of his promise,
God made a colourful rainbow in the sky.

Next Steps

Look back through the book to find more to talk about and join in with.

* Copy the actions. Do the actions with the characters – chop, saw, hammer and paint, or creep, slither, plod and hop.

* Join in with the rhyme. Pause to encourage joining in with 'Drip drop – it didn't stop!'

* Count two by two. Match the pairs of animals counting one penguin, two penguins.

* Name the colours of the rainbow together, then look back to spot the colours on other pages.

* Find shapes and sizes. Describe the animals in terms of shape or size. Look for a tall giraffe, a tiny mouse, a fat elephant and a long snake.

* Listen to Noah's noisy ark. When you see the word on the page, point and make the sound – Moo! Squawk! Oink! Ssssssss! Growl! Baa! Squeak!

Now that you've read the story... what do you remember?

* Who told Noah to build the ark?
* Why did God send the flood?
* What went into the ark?
* How long did it rain?
* Where did the ark come to rest?
* Why did God send the rainbow?

What does the story tell us?
If we listen to God, He will look after us.